Spelling and Writing

 Name: _

Table of Contents

Glossary

Adjectives: Words that tell more about nouns, such as a **happy** child, **cold** day, **hard** problem, **tall** building.

Apostrophe. A punctuation mark that shows possession (Kim's hat) or takes the place of missing letters in a word (isn't).

Command. A sentence that tells someone to do something.

Consonants. All the letters except **a**, **e**, **i**, **o**, **u**, and sometimes **y**.

Direction. A sentence that tells someone to do something; a command.

Exclamation. A sentence that shows strong feeling or excitement.

Fact. A true statement. Something that can be proved.

Joining Words (Conjunctions). Words that join sentences or combine ideas: **and, but, or, because, when, after, so.**

Noun. A word that names a person, place, or thing.

Opinion. What someone thinks or believes.

Paragraph. A group of sentences that tells about one main idea.

Plural. A word that refers to more than one thing, such as a plural noun or a plural verb.

Possessive Nouns. Nouns that show something belongs to them, such as **Jill's book.**

Prefix. One or two syllables added to the beginning of a word to change its meaning.

Question. A sentence that asks something.

Sentence. A group of words that expresses a complete thought; it must have a noun (subject) and a verb.

Singular. A word that refers to only one thing, such as a singular noun or a singular verb.

Statement. A sentence that tells something.

Suffix. One or two syllables added to the end of a word.

Support Sentence. A sentence that provides details about the topic sentence of a paragraph.

Syllable. A word—or part of a word—with only one vowel sound.

Synonym. A word that means the same thing as another word.

Topic Sentence. The sentence that tells the main idea of a paragraph.

Verb. The action word in a sentence; the word that tells what something does or that something exists.

Vowels. The letters **a**, **e**, **i**, **o**, **u**, and sometimes **y**.

Spelling Words With Long e And Long a

Long **e** is written /ē/. It can be spelled **ea** as in r**ea**l or **ee** as in d**ee**r. Long **a** is written /ā/. It can be spelled **a** as in **a**pron, **ai** as in p**ai**l, **ay** as in p**ay**, or **a**-consonant-**e** as in l**a**k**e**.

Directions: Answer the questions with words from the word box.

deal	clay	grade	weave	stream	pain	tape	sneeze	claim	treat

1. Write each word in the row that has its vowel sound.

/ā/   _____ _____ _____ _____ _____

/ē/   _____ _____ _____ _____ _____

2. Finish these sentences, using a word with the vowel sound given. Use each word from the word box only once.

Everyone in /ā/ _____ four ate an ice cream /ē/ _____ .

Every time I /ē/ _____ , I feel /ā/ _____ in my chest.

When I /ē/ _____ with yarn, I put a piece of /ā/ _____

on the loose ends so they won't come undone.

You /ā/ _____ you got a good /ē/ _____ on

your new bike, but I still think you paid too much.

We camped beside a /ē/ _____ .

We forgot to wrap up our /ā/ _____ , and it dried out.

Name: _____

Telling The Nouns From The Verbs

A noun names a person, place, or thing. Many verbs show action: **write, sing, plan,** and so on. Other verbs simply show that something "is": The dogs **are** here. The car **was** green. Some words are used as nouns one time and verbs other times.

Directions: Write one of the words from the word box in both sentences in each pair. Write an **N** over the word when it is used as a noun and a **V** over the word when it is used as a verb.

Like this: V   N

        The girl **sneezes**.   Her **sneeze** scares the dog.

sneeze	claim	grade	date	tape	treat	stream	deal

1. I _____ around dogs. My _____ is louder than your _____ .

2. Let's go buy a _____ at the store. Today I will _____ you to a candy bar.

3. Sometimes we _____ our own papers. I always get a higher

    _____ when the teacher_____ them.

4. The rain _____ down the window.   The _____ behind our

    house is overflowing.

5. Please _____ that TV show for me. I will watch the _____

    when I come home.

6. A boy in my class _____ I took his candy bar. I know his _____

    is wrong. He ate it himself.

7. My brother has a _____ tonight. He _____ the girl who lives next door.

8. Please_____the cards. While we play, I'll tell you about the_____

    I made with my sister. She's going to pay me to do her chores.

Name: _____

Hearing Those Vowels

Directions: Follow the directions below.

1. Read each word at the left. Then circle the word in the row that has the same vowel sound.

Like this:

deal	pail	church	(greet)	stove
pain	free	frame	twice	whole
weave	grape	stripe	least	thrill
grade	teach	case	joke	leave
treat	greed	throw	tent	truck

2. Write a word from the word box that rhymes with each of these.

deal	clay	grade	weave	stream	pain	tape	sneeze	claim	treat

lame _____   shape _____

May _____   feel _____

cream _____   leave _____

laid _____   drain _____

feet _____   trees _____

3. Write the word from the word box that sounds like:

/klā/ _____   /klām/ _____

/wēv/ _____   /trēt/ _____

/dēl/ _____   /grād/ _____

/strēm/ _____   /pān/ _____

/tāp/ _____   /snēz/ _____

Name: _____

Using Fewer Words

Directions: Make each pair of sentences into one sentence. Notice how commas are used in the example.

Like this:

After school Jerry ate some chocolate ice cream. It's his favorite treat.

Jerry ate his favorite treat, ice cream, after school.

1. Benny keeps sneezing.   Benny is my brother.

_____

2. Kelly was dealing the cards.   Kelly is my cousin.

_____

3. Chris is in grade ten.   Chris is my babysitter.

_____

4. Anna has a pain in her hand.   Anna is my neighbor.

_____

5. I have two tapes of the Lipsticks.   The Lipsticks are my favorite singing group.

_____

6. Jenny likes to play in the stream.   Jenny is my sister.

_____

7. Rachel brought me a treat.   Rachel is my good friend.

_____

8. Judy Blume wrote this book.   She is a very popular author.

_____

9. Mr. Thomas gave me this clay.   Mr. Thomas is my teacher.

_____

10. I'm going to weave a rug in blue and white.   Those are the colors in my bedroom.

_____

Telling What Already Happened

To write about something that already happened, we can add **ed** to the verb.

Like this: Yesterday we talk**ed**.

We can also use was and were and add **ing** to the verb.

Like this: Yesterday we **were** talk**ing**.

When a verb ends with **e**, usually we drop the **e** before adding **ing**.

Like this: grade — was grading   weave — were weaving
                   tape — was taping   sneeze — were sneezing

Directions: Write two sentences for each verb below. Tell about something that already happened and write the verb both ways. (Watch the spelling of the verbs that end with **e**.)

Like this:

stream

The rain streamed down the window._____

The rain was streaming down the window._____

grade

_____

_____

tape

_____

_____

weave

_____

_____

sneeze

_____

_____

Putting Ideas Together

Directions: Make each pair of sentences into one sentence.

Like this: Jim will deal the cards one at a time.   Jim will give four cards to everyone.

Jim will deal the cards one at a time and give four cards to everyone.

1. Amy won the contest.   Amy claimed the prize.

_____

_____

2. We need to find the scissors.   We need to buy some tape.

_____

_____

3. The stream runs through the woods.   The stream empties into the river.

_____

_____

4. Katie tripped on the steps.   Katie has a pain in her foot.

_____

_____

5. Grandpa took me to the store.   Grandpa bought me a treat.

_____

_____

Name: _____

Review

Directions: Circle the letters that spell the two /ē/ vowels and three /ā/ vowels in the sentence below.

K a y   n e e d s   i c e   c r e a m   t o   g o   w i t h   h e r   p l a i n   c a k e.

Directions: Combine these sentences. Change the verb to use **was** or **were** and add **ing** to it. Two words are highlighted in each sentence. Write **N** over the noun and **V** over the verb.

Like this:

                    V   N

My dad **taped** a TV **show**. It was a football game.

My dad was taping a TV show, a football game.

1. John **paddled** down the **stream**. John was our guide.

_____

2. He **weaved** a placemat. It was a **present** for his grandmother.

_____

3. Pete **claimed** he won the **game**. Pete is my neighbor.

_____

4. My **sister treated** us to ice cream. My sister's name is Polly.

_____

5. Maria **sneezed** while we were at the **fair**. Maria is my cousin.

_____

6. Julie and Kim **pounded** the **clay**. They are my twin sisters.

_____

7. Bobby **complained** about a **pain** in his foot. Bobby is the pitcher on our team.

_____

Spelling Words With Long i And Long o

Long **i** is written /ī/. It can be spelled **i** as in w**i**ld, **igh** as in n**igh**t, **i**-consonant-**e** as in w**i**p**e**, or **y** as in tr**y**.

Long **o** is written /ō/. It can be spelled **o** as in m**o**st, **oa** as in t**oa**st, **ow** as in thr**ow**, or **o**-consonant-**e** as in h**o**p**e**.

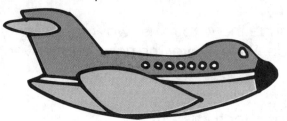 

Directions: Answer the questions with words from the word box.

stripe	groan	glow	toast	grind	fry	sight	stove	toad	flight

1. Write each word in the row that has its vowel sound.

/ī/ _____

/ō/ _____

2. Finish these sentences, using a word with the vowel sound given. Use each word from the word box only once.

We will /ī/ _____ potatoes on the /ō/ _____ .

I thought I heard a low /ō/_____ , but when I looked, there was nothing

in /ī/ _____ .

The airplane for our /ī/ _____ had a /ī/_____ painted on its side.

I saw a strange /ō/ _____ coming from the bread while making

/ō/ _____ .

Do /ō/ _____ live in the water like frogs?

We need to /ī/ _____ up the nuts into pieces before we put them in cookies.

Name: _____

Putting More Ideas Together

Directions: Make each pair of sentences into one sentence. (You might have to change the verbs for some sentences—from **is** to **are**, for example.)

Like this: Our house was flooded.   Our car was flooded.

Our house and car were flooded. _____

1. Kenny sees a glow.   Carrie sees a glow.

_____

2. Our new stove came today.   Our new refrigerator came today.

_____

3. The pond is full of toads.   The field is full of toads.

_____

4. Stripes are on the flag.   Stars are on the flag.

_____

5. The ducks took flight.   The geese took flight.

_____

6. Joe reads stories.   Dana reads stories.

_____

7. French fries will make you fat.   Milkshakes will make you fat.

_____

8. Justine heard someone groan.   Kevin heard someone groan.

_____

Name: _____

Practicing Plurals

You know how to add s to most nouns to make them plural.

Like this: one book — two books   one house — four houses

You also know that words ending with **s, ss, sh, ch,** and **x** need **es** to make them plural.

Like this: one class — two class**es**   one church — three church**es**
                    one box — four box**es**   one crash — five crash**es**

If a word ends with a consonant and **y**, you drop the **y** and add **ies**.

Like this: one cherry — two cherr**ies**   one daisy — three dais**ies**

But if the word ends with a vowel and **y**, you just add **s**.

Like this: one monkey — four monkey**s**   one key — eight key**s**

Directions: Write in the singular or plural form that is missing for each word.

Singular	Plural	Singular	Plural
Like this:			
mattress	mattresses	candy	candies
	bushes	try	
sandwich			turkeys
fry		copy	
	crosses		factories
marsh			foxes
	supplies	ax	
donkey		berry	
	stoves	day	

Name: _____

Adding Adjectives

Adjectives tell more about nouns. Adjectives are words that help explain what you mean. Here are some examples: **scary** animals, **bright** glow, **wet** frog.

Directions: Add at least two adjectives to each sentence below. Use your own words or words from the box.

pale faint	soft shivering	sticky slippery	burning gleaming	furry gentle	glistening foggy	peaceful tangled

Like this: The stripe was blue.

<u>The wide stripe was light blue.</u>

1. The frog had eyes.

_____

2. The house was a sight.

_____

3. A boy heard a groan.

_____

4. The girl tripped over a toad.

_____

5. A tiger ran through the room.

_____

6. They saw a glow in the window.

_____

7. A pan was sitting on the stove.

_____

8. The boys were eating French fries.

_____

Doing Math To Spell New Words

Directions: For each word below, take away the vowel or consonant sound and add the new sound in its place to make a new word. The spelling of the whole word will change.

Like this:

bone   - /ō/ + /ē/   =   bean   _____

toad   - /ō/ + /ī/   =   _____

sight   - /ī/ + /ē/   =   _____

fry   - /ī/ + /ē/   =   _____

groan   - /ō/ + /ē/   =   _____

mine   - /ī/ + /ō/   =   _____

stove   - /ō/ + /ē/   =   _____ (boy's name)

groan   - /ō/ + /ā/   =   _____

flight   - /ī/ + /ō/   =   _____

sight   - /s/ + /k/   =   _____

toad   - /t/ + /sh/   =   _____

fry   - /f/ + /k/   =   _____

Name: _____

Telling More

Directions: Finish these sentences by adding words that tell who, what, where, or when. Use your imagination, words from the word boxes, and any other words you need. Make some words plural and don't forget to add adjectives.

who or what

tiger   stripe
someone   groan
friend   glow
sister   toad
brother   stove

where

out of sight
behind the door
far away
very close
up the stairs

when

early in the morning
when I wasn't looking
late at night
before I got there
when the moon was full

Like this: They noticed   a green glow   behind the pine trees.
                              (what)   (where)

1. _____ shifted across the room _____
       (who or what)

_____
    (when)

2. The shadow covered _____
                                 (what)

_____
    (where)

3. The door _____ opened _____
      (where)

_____
    (when)

4. _____ hurried _____
      (who or what)   (where)

_____
    (when)

5. _____ stopped the _____
      (who or what)   (what)

_____
    (when)

Name: _____

Figuring Out Puzzles

Directions: Write the word that answers each question in the spaces with the same number. The answers all have /ō/ or /ī/ sounds in them. If you need help with spelling look on page 10.

Across
Which word:
2. Starts like toe and rhymes with most?
4. Sounds the same as grown?
6. Starts like stop and rhymes with cove?
7. Starts like flip and rhymes with kite?

Down
Which word:
1. Starts like green and rhymes with find?
3. Starts like stop and rhymes with type?
5. Starts like tea and rhymes with rode?
6. Starts like season and rhymes with bite?
7. Starts like feather and rhymes with pie?

ANSWER KEY

*This Answer Key has been designed so that
it may be easily removed if you so desire.*

GRADE 4 SPELLING & WRITING

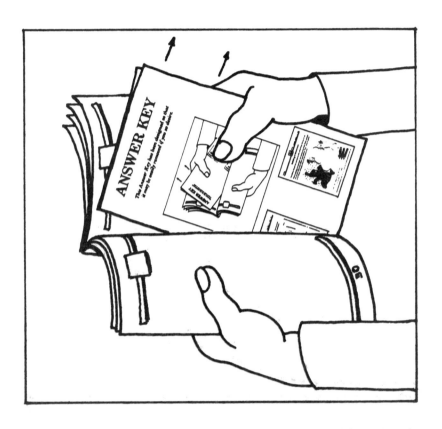

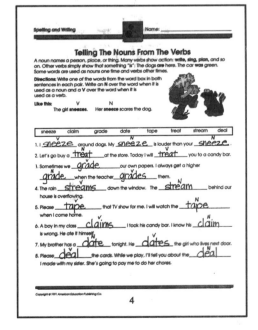

Worksheet page 3

Spelling and Writing   Name: _____

Spelling Words With Long e And Long a

Long **e** is written /ē/. It can be spelled **ea** as in real or **ee** as in deer. Long **a** is written /ā/. It can be spelled **a** as in apron, **ai** as in pail, **ay** as in pay, or **a-consonant-e** as in lake.

Directions: Answer the questions with words from the word box.

deal	clay	grade	weave	stream	pain	tape	sneeze	claim	treat

1. Write each word in the row that has its vowel sound.

/ā/   clay   grade   pain   tape   claim

/ē/   deal   weave   stream   sneeze   treat

2. Finish these sentences, using a word with the vowel sound given. Use each word from the word box only once.

Everyone in /ā/ _grade_ four ate an ice cream /ē/ _treat_ .

Every time I /ē/ _sneeze_ , I feel /ā/ _pain_ in my chest.

When I /ē/ _weave_ with yarn, I put a piece of /ā/ _tape_ on the loose ends so they won't come undone.

You /ā/ _claim_ you got a good /ē/ _deal_ on your new bike, but I still think you paid too much.

We camped beside a /ē/ _stream_ .

We forgot to wrap up our /ā/ _clay_ , and it dried out.

Copyright © 1991 American Education Publishing Co.

3

Worksheet page 4

Spelling and Writing   Name: _____

Telling The Nouns From The Verbs

A noun names a person, place, or thing. Many verbs show action: **write**, **sing**, **plan**, and so on. Other verbs simply show that something "is": The dogs **are** here. The car **was** green. Some words are used as nouns one time and verbs other times.

Directions: Write one of the words from the word box in both sentences in each pair. Write an N over the word when it is used as a noun and a V over the word when it is used as a verb.

Like this:
    N
The girl **sneezes**.   Her **sneeze** scares the dog.

sneeze	claim	grade	date	tape	treat	stream	deal

1. I _sneeze_ around dogs. My _sneeze_ is louder than your _sneeze_ .

2. Let's go buy a _treat_ at the store. Today I will _treat_ you to a candy bar.

3. Sometimes we _grade_ our own papers. I always get a higher _grade_ when the teacher _grades_ them.

4. The rain _streams_ down the window. The _stream_ behind our house is overflowing.

5. Please _tape_ that TV show for me. I will watch the _tape_ when I come home.

6. A boy in my class _claims_ I took his candy bar. I know his _claim_ is wrong. He ate it himself.

7. My brother has a _date_ tonight. He _dates_ the girl who lives next door.

8. Please _deal_ the cards. While we play, I'll tell you about the _deal_ I made with my sister. She's going to pay me to do her chores.

Copyright © 1991 American Education Publishing Co.

4

Hearing Those Vowels

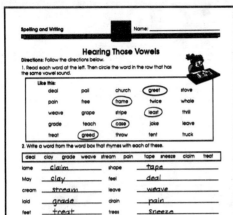

Directions: Follow the directions below.

1. Read each word at the left. Then circle the word in the row that has the same vowel sound.

Like this:

deal	pail	church	(greet)	stove
pain	free	(frame)	twice	whole
weave	grape	stripe	(least)	thrill
grade	teach	(case)	joke	leave
treat	(greed)	throw	tent	truck

2. Write a word from the word box that rhymes with each of these.

word box: deal clay grade weave stream pain tape sneeze claim treat

lame	_claim_	shape	_tape_
May	_clay_	feel	_deal_
cream	_stream_	leave	_weave_
laid	_grade_	drain	_pain_
feet	_treat_	trees	_sneeze_

3. Write the word from the word box that sounds like:

/klā/	_clay_	/klām/	_claim_
/wēv/	_weave_	/trēt/	_treat_
/dēl/	_deal_	/grād/	_grade_
/strēm/	_stream_	/pān/	_pain_
/tāp/	_tape_	/snēz/	_sneeze_

5

Putting Ideas Together

Directions: Make each pair of sentences into one sentence.

Like this: Jim will deal the cards one at a time.   Jim will give four cards to everyone.

Jim will deal the cards one at a time and give four cards to everyone.

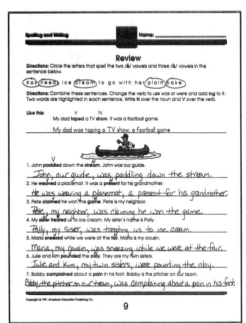

1. Amy won the contest.   Amy claimed the prize.

Amy won the contest and claimed the prize.

2. We need to find the scissors.   We need to buy some tape.

We need to find the scissors and buy some tape.

3. The stream runs through the woods.   The stream empties into the river.

The stream runs through the woods and empties into the river.

4. Katie tripped on the steps.   Katie has a pain in her foot.

Katie tripped on the steps and has a pain in her foot.

5. Grandpa took me to the store.   Grandpa bought me a treat.

Grandpa took me to the store and bought me a treat.

8

Using Fewer Words

Directions: Make each pair of sentences into one sentence. Notice how commas are used in the example.

Like this:

After school Jerry ate some chocolate ice cream. It's his favorite treat.

Jerry ate his favorite treat, ice cream, after school.

1. Benny keeps sneezing.   Benny is my brother.

Benny, my brother, keeps sneezing.

2. Kelly was dealing the cards.   Kelly is my cousin.

Kelly, my cousin, was dealing the cards.

3. Chris is in grade ten.   Chris is my babysitter.

Chris, my babysitter, is in grade ten.

4. Anna has a pain in her hand.   Anna is my neighbor.

Anna, my neighbor, has a pain in her hand.

5. I have two tapes of the Lipsticks.   The Lipsticks are my favorite singing group.

I have two tapes of the Lipsticks, my favorite singing group.

6. Jenny likes to play in the stream.   Jenny is my sister.

Jenny, my sister, likes to play in the stream.

7. Rachel brought me a treat.   Rachel is my good friend.

Rachel, my good friend, brought me a treat.

8. Judy Blume wrote this book.   She is a very popular author.

Judy Blume, a very popular author, wrote this book.

9. Mr. Thomas gave me this clay.   Mr. Thomas is my teacher.

Mr. Thomas, my teacher, gave me this clay.

10. I'm going to weave a rug in blue and white.   Those are the colors in my bedroom.

I'm going to weave a rug in blue and white, the colors in my bedroom.

6

Review

Directions: Circle the letters that spell the two /ā/ vowels and three /ē/ vowels in the sentence below.

(Kay) (nee)d ice cr(ea)m to go with her pl(ai)n (ba)ke.

Directions: Combine these sentences. Change the verb to use was or were and add ing to it. Two words are highlighted in each sentence. Write N over the noun and V over the verb.

Like this:
                    V   N
My dad taped a TV show. It was a football game.

My dad was taping a TV show, a football game.

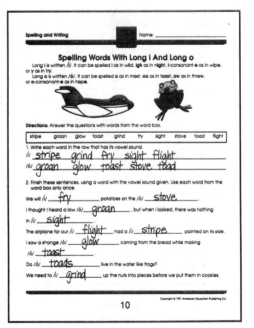

1. John paddled down the stream. John was our guide.

John, our guide, was paddling down the stream.

2. He weaved a placemat. It was a present for his grandmother.

He was weaving a placemat, a present for his grandmother.

3. Pete claimed he won the game. Pete is my neighbor.

Pete, my neighbor, was claiming he won the game.

4. My sister treated us to ice cream. My sister's name is Polly.

Polly, my sister, was treating us to ice cream.

5. Maria sneezed while we were at the fair. Maria is my cousin.

Maria, my cousin, was sneezing while we were at the fair.

6. Julie and Kim pounded the clay. They are my twin sisters.

Julie and Kim, my twin sisters, were pounding the clay.

7. Bobby complained about a pain in his foot. Bobby is the pitcher on our team.

Bobby, the pitcher on our team, was complaining about a pain in his foot.

9

Telling What Already Happened

To write about something that already happened, we can add ed to the verb.

Like this: Yesterday we talked.

We can also use was and were and add ing to the verb.

Like this: Yesterday we were talking.

When a verb ends with e, usually we drop the e before adding ing.

Like this: grade — was grading   weave — were weaving
             tape — was taping   sneeze — were sneezing

Directions: Write two sentences for each verb below. Tell about something that already happened and write the verb both ways. (Watch the spelling of the verbs that end with e.)

Like this: stream

The rain streamed down the window.

The rain was streaming down the window.

grade   _sentences will vary_

_____

tape

verbs: _taped   was/were taping_

weave

verbs: _weaved or wove   was/were weaving_

sneeze

verbs: _sneezed   was/were sneezing_

7

Spelling Words With Long i And Long o

Long i is written /ī/. It can be spelled i as in wild, igh as in night, i-consonant-e as in wipe, or y as in try.

Long o is written /ō/. It can be spelled o as in most, oa as in toast, ow as in throw, or o-consonant-e as in hope.

Directions: Answer the questions with words from the word box.

word box: stripe groan glow toast grind fry sight stove toad flight

1. Write each word in the row that has its vowel sound.

/ī/ _stripe   grind   fry   sight   flight_
/ō/ _groan   glow   toast   stove   toad_

2. Finish these sentences, using a word with the vowel sound given. Use each word from the word box only once.

We will /ī/ _fry_ potatoes on the /ō/ _stove_.

I thought I heard a low /ō/ _groan_, but when I looked, there was nothing in /ī/ _sight_.

The airplane for our /ī/ _flight_ had a /ī/ _stripe_ painted on its side.

I saw a strange /ō/ _glow_ coming from the bread while making /ō/ _toast_.

Do /ō/ _toads_ live in the water like frogs?

We need to /ī/ _grind_ up the nuts into pieces before we put them in cookies.

10

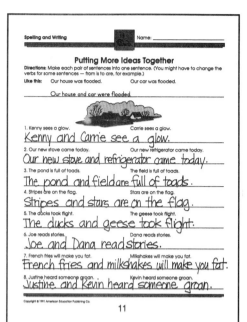

Putting More Ideas Together

Directions: Make each pair of sentences into one sentence. (You might have to change the verbs for some sentences — from is to are, for example.)
Like this: Our house was flooded.   Our car was flooded.

Our house and car were flooded.

1. Kenny sees a glow.   Carrie sees a glow.
Kenny and Carrie see a glow.

2. Our new stove came today.   Our new refrigerator came today.
Our new stove and refrigerator came today.

3. The pond is full of toads.   The field is full of toads.
The pond and field are full of toads.

4. Stripes are on the flag.   Stars are on the flag.
Stripes and stars are on the flag.

5. The ducks took flight.   The geese took flight.
The ducks and geese took flight.

6. Joe reads stories.   Dana reads stories.
Joe and Dana read stories.

7. French fries will make you fat.   Milkshakes will make you fat.
French fries and milkshakes will make you fat.

8. Justine heard someone groan.   Kevin heard someone groan.
Justine and Kevin heard someone groan.

11

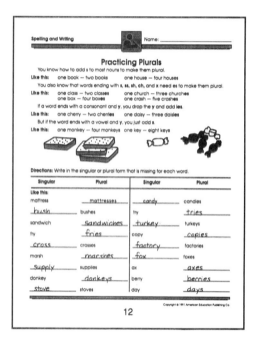

Practicing Plurals

You know how to add s to most nouns to make them plural.
Like this: one book — two books   one house — four houses
You also know that words ending with s, ss, sh, ch, and x need es to make them plural.
Like this: one class — two classes   one church — three churches
   one box — four boxes   one crash — five crashes
If a word ends with a consonant and y, you drop the y and add ies.
Like this: one cherry — two cherries   one daisy — three daisies
But if the word ends with a vowel and y, you just add s.
Like this: one monkey — four monkeys   one key — eight keys

Directions: Write in the singular or plural form that is missing for each word.

Singular	Plural	Singular	Plural
Like this:			
mattress	*mattresses*	*candy*	candies
bush	bushes	fry	*fries*
sandwich	*sandwiches*	*turkey*	turkeys
fry	*fries*	copy	*copies*
cross	crosses	*factory*	factories
marsh	*marshes*	*fox*	foxes
supply	supplies	ax	*axes*
donkey	*donkeys*	berry	*berries*
stove	stoves	day	*days*

12

Adding Adjectives

Adjectives tell more about nouns. Adjectives are words that help explain what you mean. Here are some examples: **scary** animals, **bright** glow, **wet** frog.
Directions: Add at least two adjectives to each sentence below. Use your own words or words from the box.

pale	soft	sticky	burning	furry	glistening	peaceful
faint	shivering	slippery	gleaming	gentle	foggy	tangled

Like this: The stripe was blue.
   The wide stripe was light blue.

1. The frog had eyes.
sentence additions will vary

2. The house was a sight.

3. A boy heard a groan.

4. The girl tripped over a toad.

5. A tiger ran through the room.

6. They saw a glow in the window.

7. A pan was sitting on the stove.

8. The boys were eating French fries.

13

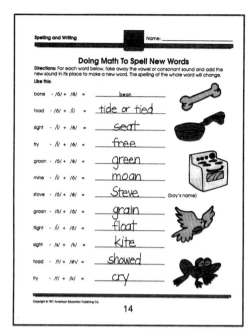

Doing Math To Spell New Words

Directions: For each word below, take away the vowel or consonant sound and add the new sound in its place to make a new word. The spelling of the whole word will change.

Like this:

bone	- /ō/ + /ē/ =	*bean*
toad	- /ō/ + /ī/ =	*tide or tied*
sight	- /ī/ + /ē/ =	*seat*
fry	- /ī/ + /ē/ =	*free*
groan	- /ō/ + /ē/ =	*green*
mine	- /ī/ + /ō/ =	*moan*
stove	- /ō/ + /ē/ =	*Steve* (boy's name)
groan	- /ō/ + /ā/ =	*grain*
flight	- /ī/ + /ō/ =	*float*
sight	- /s/ + /k/ =	*kite*
toad	- /t/ + /sh/ =	*showed*
fry	- /f/ + /k/ =	*cry*

14

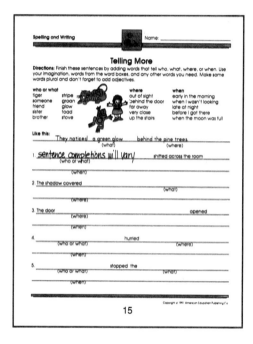

Telling More

Directions: Finish these sentences by adding words that tell who, what, where, or when. Use your imagination, words from the word boxes, and any other words you need. Make some words plural and don't forget to add adjectives.

who or what		where	when
tiger	stripe	out of sight	early in the morning
someone	groan	behind the door	when I wasn't looking
friend	glow	far away	late at night
sister	toad	very close	before I got there
brother	stove	up the stairs	when the moon was full

Like this: They noticed   a green glow   behind the pine trees
                              (what)   (where)

1. *sentence completions will vary*   shifted across the room
   ____ (who or what) ____
   ____ (when) ____

2. The shadow covered ____
   ____ (what) ____
   ____ (where) ____

3. The door ____   opened
   ____ (where) ____
   ____ (when) ____

4. ____   hurried
   (who or what)   ____ (where) ____
   ____ (when) ____

5. ____   stopped the ____
   (who or what)   ____ (what) ____
   ____ (when) ____

15

Figuring Out Puzzles

Directions: Write the word that answers each question in the spaces with the same number. The answers all have /ō/ or /ī/ sounds in them. If you need help with spelling, look on page 127.

Across
Which word:
2. Starts like toe and rhymes with most?
4. Sounds the same as grown?
6. Starts like stop and rhymes with cove?
7. Starts like flip and rhymes with kite?

Down
Which word:
1. Starts like green and rhymes with find?
3. Starts like stop and rhymes with type?
5. Starts like tea and rhymes with ride?
6. Starts like season and rhymes with bite?
7. Starts like feather and rhymes with pie?

16

Review

Directions: Circle the letters that spell three /ō/ vowels and four /ī/ vowels in the sentence below.

Mike hopes his yellow coat will dry by tonight.

Directions: Pretend something scary happened and you are asked to write about it for your school newspaper.
Follow these steps:
1. Write all your ideas in any order on another sheet of paper. The words in the word box on page 17 will get you started. What could have happened? Where? Why was it scary? Who was there? What did he or she do?
2. Pick the ideas you want to use and put them in order.
3. Now write what happened in sentences, using lots of adjectives and some plurals. Combine some of the sentences, as you learned on page 18.
4. Read your sentences out loud. Will your readers understand what happened? Do you need to make any changes?
5. After you make any necessary changes, write your article below.
6. On your own paper, draw a picture to help show what happened.
7. Show someone your article and picture.

Your article:

articles will vary

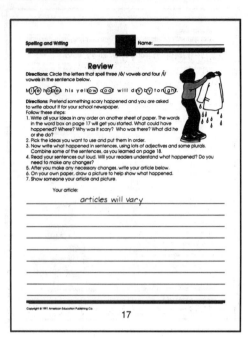

Spelling The /k/ Sound

The /k/ sound can be spelled with a **k** as in peek, **c** as in cousin, **ck** as in sick, and **ch** as in Chris. /k/ is also spelled **cc**, as in accuse. In some words, though, one **c** may be pronounced /k/ and the other one /s/, as in accident.

Directions: Answer the questions with words from the word box.

| Christmas accuse freckle castle command stomach cork rake jacket accident |

1. Which two words spell /k/ with just a k?

   cork   rake

2. Which two words spell /k/ with ck?

   freckle   jacket

3. Which two words spell /k/ with ch?

   Christmas   stomach

4. Which five words spell /k/ with c?

   accuse, command, accident, castle, cork

5. Finish these sentences, using a word with /k/ spelled the way given. Use each word from the word box only once.

Dad gave Mom a garden (k) _rake_ for (ch) _Christmas_.

There are (ck) _freckles_ on my face and (ch) _stomach_.

The people (cc) _accuse_ her of taking a (ck) _jacket_.

The police took (c) _command_ after the (cc) _accident_.

The (c) _castle_ was made out of (c and k) _cork_.

Putting Ideas Together

Joining words, such as **and, but, or, when,** and **after,** help us combine two short sentences into one more interesting sentence.
Directions: Combine each pair of sentences, using one of the joining words given.

Like this:

and / when / but   My stomach hurts. I still want to go to the movies.
   My stomach hurts, but I still want to go to the movies.

or / when / but   1. He accused me of peeking. I felt very angry.
   When he accused me of peeking, I felt very angry.

but / or / after   2. The accident was over. I started shaking.
   After the accident was over, I started shaking.

and / after / or   3. Is that a freckle? Is that dirt?
   Is that a freckle or is that dirt?

and / or / but   4. I forgot my jacket. I had to go back and get it.
   I forgot my jacket, and I had to go back and get it.

after / or / but   5. I like Christmas. I don't like waiting for it.
   I like Christmas, but I don't like waiting for it.

when / and / but   6. Would you like to live in a castle? Would you like to live on a houseboat?
   Would you like to live in a castle, or would you like to live on a houseboat?

but / when / or   7. The general gave the command. The army marched.
   When the general gave the command, the army marched.

after / or / but   8. The trees dropped all their leaves. We raked them up.
   After the trees dropped all their leaves, we raked them up.

Using Those -ing Verbs

Remember, use **is** and **are** when you are writing about something that's happening right now. Use **was** and **were** when you describe something that already happened.
Directions: Use the verb on the left to finish each sentence. Add -ing to the verb and use **is, are, was,** or **were** with it. (Don't forget: if a verb ends with **e**, drop the **e** before adding -ing: paste — pasting.)

Like this:

rake   When it started to rain, we _were raking_ the leaves.

command   When the soldiers won that battle last week, Captain Stevens _was commanding_ them.

accuse   Now the police _are accusing_ them of stealing the money.

hatch   Look! The eggs _are hatching_.

glow   A minute ago the sky _was glowing_.

treat   My dad says he _is treating_ us to ice cream!

sneeze   She _was sneezing_ the whole time we were at the mall.

grade   While we were playing outside at recess, he _was grading_ our tests.

groan   I hear something. Who _is groaning_?

grind   As I watched, the workers _were grinding_ the wood into little chips.

Making Ends Meet

Directions: Combine each pair of sentences. Choose the best joining word for those two sentences. Here are some choices: **and, but, or, when, after.**

Sentences will vary

1. I would like to live in a castle. There aren't any in our neighborhood.
   (possible joining word: but)

2. I sit in the sun. I get more freckles.
   (and, when, after)

3. The teacher gives a command. Everyone changes places.
   (and, when, after)

4. Does cork come from trees? Is it man-made?
   (or)

5. I tried on my old jacket. It still fits.
   (and)

6. Christmas was over. We took down our tree.
   (and, when, after)

7. I took my medicine. My stomach felt much better.
   (and, when, after)

8. I'd like to rake the leaves. It's raining now.
   (but)

Finding The Mistakes

Directions: After you circle the spelling mistakes, write the words correctly. If you have trouble spelling them, look on page 25.

1. What did you get for Cristmas this year?   Christmas

2. My aunt gave me boots and a new jackit.   jacket

3. I need to get some food in my stomack.   stomach

4. Does anyone know why korks float?   corks

5. I dropped my glass by accident.   accident

6. A comand is a sentence that tells someone to do something.   command

7. We visited a casel on our trip to Ireland.   castle

8. My big brother is always acusing me of using his stuff.   accusing

9. I lost my rak under all the leaves.   rake

10. I wish I had as many frekles as you.   freckles

Now it's your turn! Make up five sentences, using a /k/ word in each one. Spell the /k/ word incorrectly and see if someone else can find the mistake.

1. _Sentences will vary_
2. _____
3. _____
4. _____
5. _____

Knowing When To Stop

Sentences without periods are difficult to read.

Directions: In the paragraph below, use periods, question marks, or exclamation marks to show where one sentence stops and the next begins. Circle the first letter of each new sentence to show that it should be a capital.

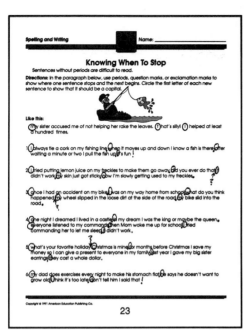

Like this:

My sister accused me of not helping her rake the leaves. That's silly! I helped at least a hundred times.

1. I always tie a cork on my fishing line when it moves up and down I know a fish is there after waiting a minute or two I pull the fish up it's fun

2. I tried putting lemon juice on my freckles to make them go away did you ever do that it didn't work my skin just got sticky now I'm slowly getting used to my freckles

3. Once I had an accident on my bike I was on my way home from school what do you think happened my wheel slipped in the loose dirt at the side of the road my bike slid into the road

4. One night I dreamed I lived in a castle in my dream I was the king or maybe the queen everyone listened to my commands then Mom woke me up for school I tried commanding her she didn't work

5. What's your favorite holiday Christmas is mine four months before Christmas I save my money so I can give a present to everyone in my family last year I gave my big sister earrings they cost a whole dollar

6. My dad does exercises every night to make his stomach flat he says he doesn't want to grow old I think it's too late don't tell him I said that

---

Spelling The /f/ Sound

The /f/ sound can be spelled with an f as in fun, gh as in laugh, or ph as in phone.

Directions: Answer the questions with words from the word box.

fuss	paragraph	phone	friendship	freedom
defend	flood	alphabet	rough	laughter

1. Which three words spell /f/ with ph?

paragraph   _alphabet_   _phone_

2. Which two words spell /f/ with gh? _rough_   _laughter_

3. Which five words spell /f/ with an f? _fuss_   _friendship_

freedom   _defend_   _flood_

4. Finish these sentences, using a word with /f/ spelled the way given. Use each word from the word box only once.

I don't know why my teacher makes so much (f) _fuss_ over

writing a (ph) _paragraph_ .

A (f) _friendship_ can help you through (gh) _rough_ times.

The soldiers will (f) _defend_ our (f) _freedom_ .

Can you say the (ph) _alphabet_ backwards?

When I answered the (ph) _phone_ ,

all I could hear was (gh) _laughter_ .

If it keeps raining, we'll have a (f) _flood_ .

Figuring Out The Code

Remember that the vowels are a, e, i, o, u, and sometimes y. All the other letters are consonants.

Directions: Each picture below stands for a consonant. Write the consonants they stand for on the lines on the left. Then add vowels to spell words from the word box.

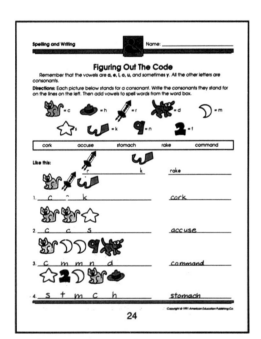

| cork | accuse | stomach | rake | command |

Like this:

r   k   _rake_

1. c   k   _cork_

2. c   c   s   _accuse_

3. c   m   m   n   d   _command_

4. s   t   m   c   h   _stomach_

Using Topic Sentences

A paragraph is a group of sentences that tell about one main idea. A topic sentence tells the main idea of a paragraph.

Many topic sentences come first in the paragraph. The topic sentence in the paragraph below is underlined. Do you see how it tells the reader what the whole paragraph is about?

Friendships can make you happy or make you sad. You feel happy to do things and go places with your friends. You get to know each other so well that you can almost read each others' minds. But friendships can be sad when your friend moves away—or decides to be best friends with someone else.

Directions: Underline the topic sentence in this paragraph:

We have two rules about using the phone at our house. Our whole family agreed on them. The first rule is not to talk longer than ten minutes. The second rule is to take good messages if you answer the phone for someone else.

Directions: After you read the paragraph below, write a topic sentence for it.

_____Sentences will vary_____

_____

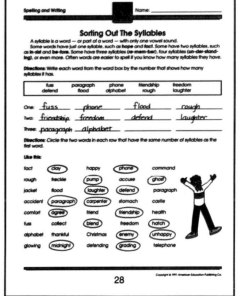

For one thing, you could ask your neighbors if they need any help. They might be willing to pay you for walking their dog or mowing their grass or weeding their garden. Maybe your older brothers or sisters would pay you to do some of their chores. You also could ask your parents if there's an extra job you could do around the house to make money.

Directions: Write a topic sentence for a paragraph on each of these subjects:

Homework: _Sentences will vary_

_____

Television: _____

_____

Using What I've Learned

Directions: Write a police report on an accident of some kind at a castle. Follow these steps:
1. Write all your ideas in any order on another sheet of paper. What happened? Who saw it? Who or what do you think caused it? Why were the police called?
2. Pick the ideas you want to use and put them in order.
3. Now write what happened in sentences. Combine some short sentences with and, but, or, after, or when. Make sure all your sentences end with a period or question mark.
4. Read your sentences out loud. Did you leave out any important facts? Will your "commanding officer" know what happened?
5. Make any necessary changes and write your report below.
6. Read your report to someone.

OFFICIAL POLICE REPORT

Reporting Officer: _____

Date of accident: _____   Time of accident: _____

_____Sentences will vary_____

_____

_____

_____

_____

_____

_____

_____

_____

_____

_____

_____

_____

Sorting Out The Syllables

A syllable is a word — or part of a word — with only one vowel sound.

Some words have just one syllable, such as hope and fact. Some have two syllables, such as in-sist and be-fore. Some have three syllables (re-mem-ber), four syllables (un-der-stand-ing), or even more. Often words are easier to spell if you know how many syllables they have.

Directions: Write each word from the word box by the number that shows how many syllables it has.

fuss	paragraph	phone	friendship	freedom
defend	flood	alphabet	rough	laughter

One: _fuss_   _phone_   _flood_   _rough_

Two: _friendship_   _freedom_   _defend_   _laughter_

Three: _paragraph_   _alphabet_   _____

Directions: Circle the two words in each row that have the same number of syllables as the first word.

Like this:

fact	(clay)	happy	(phone)	command
rough	freckle	(pump)	accuse	(ghost)
jacket	flood	(laughter)	(defend)	paragraph
accident	(paragraph)	(carpenter)	stomach	castle
comfort	(agree)	friend	(friendship)	health
fuss	collect	(blend)	freedom	(hatch)
alphabet	thankful	Christmas	(enemy)	(unhappy)
glowing	(midnight)	defending	(grading)	telephone

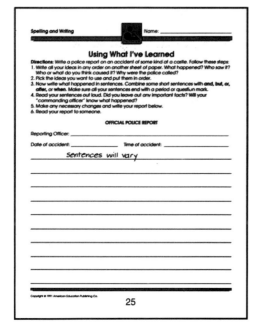

Supporting My Ideas

Supporting sentences provide details about the topic sentence of a paragraph.

Directions: In the paragraph below, underline the topic sentence. Then cross out the supporting sentence that does not belong in this paragraph.

One spring it started to rain and didn't stop for two weeks. All the rivers flooded. Some people living near the rivers had to leave their homes. Farmers couldn't plant their crops because the fields were so wet. Plants need water to grow. The sky was dark and gloomy all the time.

Directions: Write three supporting sentences to go with each topic sentence below. Make sure each supporting sentence stays on the same subject as the topic sentence.

Support sentences will vary

Not everyone should have a pet.

1. _____
2. _____
3. _____

I like to go on field trips with my class.

1. _____
2. _____
3. _____

I've been thinking about what I want to be when I get older.

1. _____
2. _____
3. _____

Copyright © 1991 American Education Publishing Co.

29

Planning Paragraphs

Each paragraph should have one main idea. If you have a lot of ideas, you need to write several paragraphs.

Directions: Read the ideas below and number them:
1. if the idea tells about Jill herself
2. if the idea tells what she did
3. if the idea tells why she did it

2	found a bird caught in a kite string
1	in grade four at Center School
2	untangled the bird
3	wouldn't want to live in a cage
1	plays outside a lot
3	knew the bird was wild
1	likes pets
2	gave the bird its freedom

Now use the ideas to write three paragraphs. Use your own paper if necessary. Write Paragraph 1 about Jill. Write Paragraph 2 about what she did. Write Paragraph 3 about why she did it.

paragraphs will vary

_____
_____
_____
_____
_____
_____
_____

Copyright © 1991 American Education Publishing Co.

31

Searching For Words

Directions: Make a word search using words from the word box. First, print the words in the spaces below making some of them cross each other. Then fill the extra spaces with other letters.

Like this:

v	n	r	p	k	
b	h	o	n	e	
d	x	u	d		
x	w	g	m	k	
o	p	h	f	b	

Then see if someone else can find the words you "hid."

fuss	paragraph	phone	friendship	freedom
defend	flood	alphabet	rough	laughter

Puzzle will vary

30

Copyright © 1991 American Education Publishing Co.

Review

Directions: On another sheet of paper, write three paragraphs that tell a story about this picture. Tell who lives in the house, what happened, and why it happened. Use your imagination. Begin each paragraph with a topic sentence that tells the main idea. Try to include some words with /f/ in them. Read your paragraphs out loud, make any necessary changes, and copy them below.

paragraphs will vary

Who lives there:

_____
_____
_____

What happened:

_____
_____
_____

Why it happened:

_____
_____
_____

Copyright © 1991 American Education Publishing Co.

32

Name: _____

Review

Directions: Circle the letters that spell three /ō/ vowels and four /ī/ vowels in the sentence below.

M i k e   h o p e s   h i s   y e l l o w   c o a t   w i l l   d r y   b y   t o n i g h t.

Directions: Pretend something scary happened and you are asked to write about it for your school newspaper.
Follow these steps:

1. Write all your ideas in any order on another sheet of paper. The words in the word box on page 10 will get you started. What could have happened? Where? Why was it scary? Who was there? What did he or she do?
2. Pick the ideas you want to use and put them in order.
3. Now write what happened in sentences using lots of adjectives and some plurals. Combine some of the sentences as you learned on page 11.
4. Read your sentences out loud. Will your readers understand what happened? Do you need to make any changes?
5. After you make any necessary changes, write your article below.
6. On your own paper, draw a picture to help you show what happened.
7. Show someone your article and picture.

Your article:

_____

_____

_____

_____

_____

_____

_____

_____

_____

_____

Name: _____

Spelling The /k/ Sound

The **/k/** sound can be spelled with a **k** as in pee**k**, **c** as in **c**ousin, **ck** as in si**ck**, and **ch** as in **Ch**ris. **/K/** is also spelled **cc**, as in a**cc**use. In some words, though, one **c** may be pronounced **/k/** and the other one **/s/**, as in a**cc**ident.

Directions: Answer the questions with words from the word box.

Christmas accuse freckle castle command stomach cork rake jacket accident

1. Which two words spell /k/ with just a **k**?

_____

2. Which two words spell /k/ with **ck**?

_____

3. Which two words spell /k/ with **ch**?

_____

4. Which five words spell /k/ with **c** or **cc**?

_____

5. Finish these sentences, using a word with /k/ spelled the way given. Use each word from the word box only once.

Dad gave Mom a garden (k) _____ for (ch) _____ .

There are (ck) _____ on my face and (ch) _____ .

The people (cc) _____ her of taking a (ck) _____ .

The police took (c) _____ after the (cc) _____ .

The (c) _____ was made out of (c and k) _____ .

Name: _____

Putting Ideas Together

Joining words, such as **and, but, or, when,** and **after,** help us combine two short sentences into one more interesting sentence.

Directions: Combine each pair of sentences using one of the joining words given.

Like this:

and
when
but

My stomach hurts. I still want to go to the movies.

<u>My stomach hurts, but I still want to go to the movies.</u>

or
when
but

1. He accused me of peeking. I felt very angry.

_____

but
or
after

2. The accident was over. I started shaking.

_____

and
after
or

3. Is that a freckle? Is that dirt?

_____

and
or
but

4. I forgot my jacket. I had to go back and get it.

_____

after
or
but

5. I like Christmas. I don't like waiting for it.

_____

when
and
or

6. Would you like to live in a castle? Would you like to live on a houseboat?

_____

but
when
or

7. The general gave the command. The army marched.

_____

after
or
but

8. The trees dropped all their leaves. We raked them up.

_____

Using Those -ing Verbs

Remember, use **is** and **are** when you are writing about something that is happening right now. Use **was** and **were** when you describe something that already happened.

Directions: Use the verb on the left to finish each sentence. Add **-ing** to the verb and use **is, are, was,** or **were** with it. (Don't forget: if a verb ends with **e**, drop the **e** before adding **-ing**: paste — are pasting.)

Like this:

rake   When it started to rain, we <u>were raking</u> the leaves.

command   When the soldiers marched up the hill last week,

Captain Stevens _____ them.

accuse   Now the police _____ them of stealing the money.

hatch   Look! The eggs _____ .

glow   A minute ago the sky_____ .

treat   My dad says he _____ us to ice cream!

sneeze   She _____ the whole time we were at the mall.

grade   While we were playing outside at recess, he _____
our tests.

groan   I hear something. Who _____ ?

grind   As I watched, the workers_____ the wood
into little chips.

20

Name: _____

Making Ends Meet

Directions: Combine each pair of sentences. Choose the best joining word for those two sentences. Here are some choices: **and, but, or, when, after.**

1. I would like to live in a castle. There aren't any in our neighborhood.

_____

2. I sit in the sun. I get more freckles.

_____

3. The teacher gives a command. Everyone changes places.

_____

4. Does cork come from trees? Is it man-made?

_____

5. I tried on my old jacket. It still fits.

_____

6. Christmas was over. We took down our tree.

_____

7. I took my medicine. My stomach felt much better.

_____

8. I'd like to rake the leaves. It's raining now.

_____

Name: _____

Finding The Mistakes

Directions: After you circle the spelling mistakes, write the words correctly. If you have trouble spelling them, look on page 18.

1. What did you get for Cristmas this year? _____

2. My aunt gave me boots and a new jaket. _____

3. I need to get some food in my stomack. _____

4. Does anyone know why korks float? _____

5. I dropped my glass by acident. _____

6. A comand is a sentence that tells someone to do something. _____

7. We visited a casel on our trip to Ireland. _____

8. My big brother is always acusing me of using his stuff. _____

9. I lost the rak under all the leaves. _____

10. I wish I had as many frekles as you. _____

Now it's your turn! Make up five sentences using a /k/ word in each one. Spell the /k/ word incorrectly and see if someone else can find the mistake.

1. _____

2. _____

3. _____

4. _____

5. _____

Knowing When To Stop

Sentences without periods are difficult to read.

Directions: In the paragraph below 'use periods, question marks, or exclamation marks to show where one sentence stops and the next begins. Circle the first letter of each new sentence to show that it should be a capital.

Like this:

(m)y sister accused me of not helping her rake the leaves. (t)hat's silly! (I) helped at least a hundred times.

1. I always tie a cork on my fishing line when it moves up and down I know a fish is there after waiting a minute or two I pull the fish up it's fun

2. I tried putting lemon juice on my freckles to make them go away did you ever do that it didn't work my skin just got sticky now I'm slowly getting used to my freckles

3. once I had an accident on my bike I was on my way home from school what do you think happened my wheel slipped in the loose dirt at the side of the road my bike slid into the road

4. one night I dreamed I lived in a castle in my dream I was the king or maybe the queen everyone listened to my commands then Mom woke me up for school I tried commanding her to let me sleep it didn't work

5. what's your favorite holiday Christmas is mine for months before Christmas I save my money so I can give a present to everyone in my family last year I gave my big sister earrings they cost a whole dollar

6. my dad does exercises every night to make his stomach flat he says he doesn't want to grow old I think it's too late don't tell him I said that

Figuring Out The Code

Remember that the vowels are **a, e, i, o, u,** and sometimes **y**. All the other letters are consonants.

Directions: Each picture below stands for a consonant. Write the consonants they stand for on the lines on the left. Then add vowels to spell words from the word box.

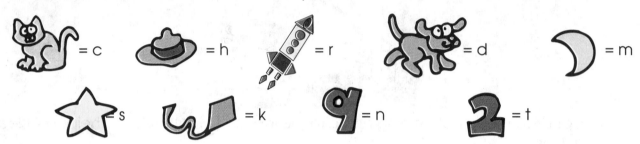

cork	accuse	stomach	rake	command

Like this:

r   k   rake

1. _____   _____

2. _____   _____

3. _____   _____

4. _____   _____

Name: _____

Review

Directions: Write a police report about an event where someone your age was a hero or heroine. Follow these steps:

1. Write all your ideas in any order on another sheet of paper. What happened? Who saw it? Who or what do you think caused it? Why were the police called?
2. Pick the ideas you want to use and put them in order.
3. Now write what happened in sentences. Combine some short sentences with **and, but, or, after,** or **when.** Make sure all your sentences end with a period or question mark.
4. Read your sentences out loud. Did you leave out any important facts? Will your "commanding officer" know what happened?
5. Make any necessary changes and write your report below.
6. Read your report to someone.

OFFICIAL POLICE REPORT

Reporting Officer: _____

Date of accident: _____   Time of accident: _____

_____

_____

_____

_____

_____

_____

_____

_____

_____

_____

Spelling The /f/ Sound

The /f/ sound can be spelled with an **f** as in **f**un, **gh** as in lau**gh**, or **ph** as in **ph**one.

Directions: Answer the questions with words from the word box.

fuss	paragraph	phone	friendship	freedom
defend	flood	alphabet	rough	laughter

1. Which three words spell /f/ with **ph**?

_____   _____   _____

2. Which two words spell /f/ with **gh**? _____   _____

3. Which five words spell /f/ with an **f**? _____   _____

_____   _____   _____

4. Finish these sentences, using a word with /f/ spelled the way given. Use each word from the word box only once.

I don't know why my teacher makes so much (f) _____ over

writing a (ph) _____ .

A (f) _____ can help you through (gh)_____ times.

The soldiers will (f) _____ our (f)_____ .

Can you say the (ph)_____ backwards?

When I answered the (ph)_____ ,

all I could hear was (gh)_____ .

If it keeps raining, we'll have a (f)_____ .

Name: _____

Using Topic Sentences

A paragraph is a group of sentences that tell about one main idea. A topic sentence tells the main idea of a paragraph.

Many topic sentences come first in the paragraph. The topic sentence in the paragraph below is underlined. Do you see how it tells the reader what the whole paragraph is about?

<u>Friendships can make you happy or make you sad.</u> You feel happy to do things and go places with your friends. You get to know each other so well that you can almost read each others' minds. But friendships can be sad when your friend moves away—or decides to be best friends with someone else.

Directions: Underline the topic sentence in this paragraph:

We have two rules about using the phone at our house. Our whole family agreed on them. The first rule is not to talk longer than ten minutes. The second rule is to take good messages if you answer the phone for someone else.

Directions: After you read the paragraph below, write a topic sentence for it.

_____

_____

_____

For one thing, you could ask your neighbors if they need any help. They might be willing to pay you for walking their dog or mowing their grass or weeding their garden. Maybe your older brothers or sisters would pay you to do some of their chores. You also could ask your parents if there's an extra job you could do around the house to make money.

Directions: Write a topic sentence for a paragraph on each of these subjects:

Homework: _____

_____

Television: _____

_____

Name: _____

Sorting Out The Syllables

A syllable is a word — or part of a word — with only one vowel sound.

Some words have just one syllable, such as **hope** and **fact**. Some have two syllables, such as **in-sist** and **be-fore**. Some have three syllables (**re-mem-ber**), four syllables (**un-der-stand-ing**), or even more. Often words are easier to spell if you know how many syllables they have.

Directions: Write each word from the word box by the number that shows how many syllables it has.

fuss	paragraph	phone	friendship	freedom
defend	flood	alphabet	rough	laughter

One: _____ _____ _____ _____

Two: _____ _____ _____ _____

Three: _____ _____ _____ _____

Directions: Circle the two words in each row that have the same number of syllables as the first word.

Like this:

fact   (clay)   happy   (phone)   command

rough   freckle   pump   accuse   ghost

jacket   flood   laughter   defend   paragraph

accident   paragraph   carpenter   stomach   castle

comfort   agree   friend   friendship   health

fuss   collect   blend   freedom   hatch

alphabet   thankful   Christmas   enemy   unhappy

glowing   midnight   defending   grading   telephone

Supporting My Ideas

Supporting sentences provide details about the topic sentence of a paragraph.

Directions: In the paragraph below, underline the topic sentence. Then cross out the supporting sentence that does not belong in this paragraph.

One spring it started to rain and didn't stop for two weeks. All the rivers flooded. Some people living near the rivers had to leave their homes. Farmers couldn't plant their crops because the fields were so wet. Plants need water to grow. The sky was dark and gloomy all the time.

Directions: Write three supporting sentences to go with each topic sentence below. Make sure each supporting sentence stays on the same subject as the topic sentence.

Not everyone should have a pet.

1. _____

2. _____

3. _____

I like to go on field trips with my class.

1. _____

2. _____

3. _____

I've been thinking about what I want to be when I get older.

1. _____

2. _____

3. _____

Name: _____

Searching For Words

Directions: Make a word search using words from the word box. First, print the words in the spaces below making some of them cross each other. Then fill the extra spaces with other letters.

Like this:

```
v   n     r   p     k
p   h     o   n     e
d   s     u   l     c
x   w     g   m     k
o   p     h   f     b
```

Then see if someone else can find the words you "hid."

fuss	paragraph	phone	friendship	freedom
defend	flood	alphabet	rough	laughter

30

Name: _____

Planning Paragraphs

Each paragraph should have one main idea. If you have a lot of ideas, you need to write several paragraphs.

Directions: Read the ideas below and number them:
   1. if the idea tells about Jill herself
   2. if the idea tells what she did
   3. if the idea tells why she did it

_____   found a bird caught in a kite string

_____   in grade four at Center School

_____   untangled the bird

_____   wouldn't want to live in a cage

_____   plays outside a lot

_____   knew the bird was wild

_____   likes pets

_____   gave the bird its freedom

Now use the ideas to write three paragraphs. Use your own paper if necessary.
Write Paragraph 1 about Jill. Write Paragraph 2 about what she did. Write Paragraph 3 about why she did it.

_____

_____

_____

_____

_____

_____

_____

_____

Review

Directions: On another sheet of paper write three paragraphs that tell a story about this picture. Tell who lives in the house, what happened, and why it happened. Use your imagination. Begin each paragraph with a topic sentence that tells the main idea. Try to include some words with /**f**/ in them. Read your paragraphs out loud, make any necessary changes, and copy them below.

Who lives there:

_____

_____

_____

_____

What happened:

_____

_____

_____

_____

Why it happened:

_____

_____

_____

_____